The Book of
KAKURO

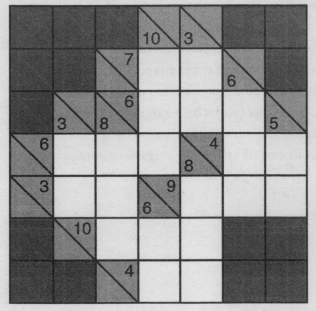

AND HOW TO SOLVE IT

D0608525

Dr Gareth Moore gained his PhD at Cambridge University in the field of machine intelligence. He is highly experienced in computer software research and development, and produced his own Kakuro creation software almost as soon as the first puzzle appeared in a British newspaper. He has a wide range of media interests and has written for both US and UK news-stand magazines. He now runs his own video production company, Cantab Films, and works on a range of puzzle and other websites, including **www.dokakuro. com** and its sister site at **www.dosudoku.com**.

The Book of
KAKURO
AND HOW TO SOLVE IT

Gareth Moore

Michael O'Mara Books Limited

First published in Great Britain in 2005 by
Michael O'Mara Books Limited
9 Lion Yard
Tremadoc Road
London SW4 7NQ

Compilation copyright © Michael O'Mara Books Limited 2005

Puzzles and solutions copyright © Gareth Moore 2005

All rights reserved.
No part of this publication may be reproduced, stored in a
retrieval system or transmitted by any means without the
prior permission in writing of the publisher, nor be otherwise
circulated in any form of binding or cover other than that in
which it is published and without a similar condition including
this condition being imposed on the subsequent purchaser.

A CIP catalogue record for this book is
available from the British Library

ISBN 1-84317-200-3

1 3 5 7 9 10 8 6 4 2

www.mombooks.com

www.dokakuro.com

Designed and typeset by www.glensaville.com

Printed and bound in Great Britain by
Cox & Wyman, Reading, Berks

INTRODUCTION

Kakuro, the name of which derives from a contraction of the Japanese word for 'addition' and the Japanese pronunciation of the English word 'cross', is a puzzle and logic game that's simple to learn and yet challenging to master. It can perhaps be thought of as a crossword puzzle featuring numbers rather than letters; it's appropriate, then, that in the US Kakuro is known as Cross Sums.

But there's more to Kakuro than this. It can also be compared to Sudoku, the number-placing puzzle craze, because repeating a digit is forbidden within a clue area, and the only valid digits are the numbers 1 to 9.

And, just like Sudoku, you don't need to be a mathematical genius to solve Kakuro puzzles. In fact, you don't need to do any maths at all, because we've included a list of all the sums you'll ever need to play every puzzle in this book. What are you waiting for?

HOW TO PLAY

The grids vary in size but they all work
the same way. Each puzzle is made up of a
combination of solid and 'clue' squares, as
well as empty squares grouped into discrete
units, each called a 'run', the aim being to fill
each empty square with a single digit from
1 to 9. Zero is never a valid digit, and within
each run a figure must not appear twice.

Unlike crosswords, the clues of a Kakuro
puzzle are contained inside each grid, so
you don't need to keep looking away as
you solve the puzzle. Each horizontal and
vertical 'run' of empty squares starts with a
shaded 'clue' square, positioned immediately
to its left (for horizontal runs), or above (for
vertical runs); a run ends when stopped by
a solid square or another clue square. A clue
square is split in two by a diagonal line, and
will contain either one or two numbers, each
called a 'clue'. The clue positioned above
the diagonal line gives the total that all the
digits in that horizontal run must add up
to; similarly, the clue number below the
diagonal line in a clue square positioned
above a vertical run gives the sum that the

empty squares *below* that clue must equal.

What gives the puzzles their fun and fascinating twist is that no digit can be repeated within a single vertical or horizontal run. So, for example, a 4 cannot be formed from the digits 2 and 2, but can only be made from 1 and 3. This means that logical reasoning is required to establish which digits will fit where.

SOLVING A PUZZLE

It doesn't take very long before combinations of clues can be spotted that allow the solving of the puzzle to begin. For example, in the grid below, note that in the bottom-left empty square the clues 4 (down) and 3 (across) overlap in the box here labelled 'a':

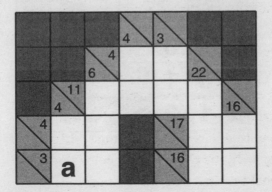

It's clear that 1 and 2 is a valid combination to make 3, and that 1 and 3 is a valid combination for making 4. This means that box 'a' must contain one of 1, 2 or 3. But if it contained 3 then there would be no valid combination for the clue '3' since 0 cannot be used, and if it contained 2 then there would be no valid combination for the clue '4' since we cannot use the same digit twice (i.e. 2 and 2). Therefore, it can only be 1.

Following this reasoning, if 'a' is 1 then the cell above must contain 3 (since 1 + 3 equals 4) and similarly the cell on its right must contain 2. This can also be applied to the two cells above. The illustration below demonstrates these steps:

Now, the same reasoning about valid totals for 3 and 4 can be applied to solve the top section of the puzzle:

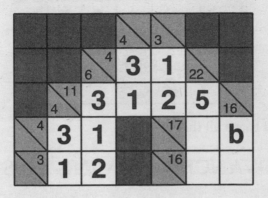

And, finally, the bottom-right part can be solved in a similar way. Notice that 16 can only be made up of 7 and 9, since 8 and 8 would repeat the same digit, while other combinations such as 6 and 10 are invalid because only numbers 1 to 9 can be used. Similarly, 17 must be made up of 8 and 9. The only common digit in this case is 9, so the cell, above labelled 'b', must be 9.

Solving the remainder of the puzzle can be achieved using simple mathematics:

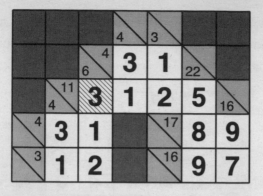

And that's all there is to it!

ADVANCED SOLVING TIPS

Thinking about valid digit combinations is
all that is required to solve the puzzles in this
book, but there are some tricks that will help
too. And, while it may sound obvious, use a
pencil to mark in the possible combinations
of numbers for each empty square, which
can then be eliminated as you go along.

ADDING UP AREAS

Knowing that the total of the digits in the grid
as a whole (excluding the clues) is always the
same whether you add them up horizontally
or vertically can help to solve small areas of
the puzzle. For example, in the grid above,
the horizontal clues at bottom left are 4 and

3, which total 7. The clues running down into this bottom-left area are 4 and 6, totalling 10. The difference between the sum of the vertical and horizontal clues (10 - 7) is 3, and 3 will be the value of the cell that is in one area but not the other. This is indeed the case, and can be seen above in the hatched square.

ELIMINATING DIGIT PAIRS

If you have worked out that a run consists of, for example, only a 1 or a 3 in one square and only a 1 or a 3 in another square, then it follows that there *cannot* be a 1 or a 3 anywhere else in the run, since between the two cells both digits are already accounted for.

THE PUZZLES IN THIS BOOK

You should never need to guess when solving the puzzles in this book – *all* of them can be solved by thinking about the possible orders of digits within each run and making certain eliminations based on this. On the other hand, when you've only got a couple of options for a square sometimes guessing works very well – but it's never compulsory!

There are five difficulty levels – Easy (Level 1), Moderate (Level 2), Difficult (Level 3), Very Hard (Level 4) and Extreme (Level 5). The Easy puzzles require simpler logic-solving than the later puzzles, so they're a good place to get the hang of things. The Extreme puzzles are for when you've truly mastered the art of Kakuro! If you can solve them without guessing then you are doing very well.

Each puzzle has a unique solution, which is given at the back of the book.

VALID DIGIT COMBINATIONS

These lists of valid number combinations for a given clue total, and for clue lengths of 2, 3, 4, 5 and 6 squares, are useful for working out which digits may work in certain runs.

CLUES OF LENGTH 2:

To make:	Combinations:
3:	1,2;
4:	1,3;
5:	1,4; 2,3;
6:	1,5; 2,4;
7:	1,6; 2,5; 3,4;
8:	1,7; 2,6; 3,5;
9:	1,8; 2,7; 3,6; 4,5;
10:	1,9; 2,8; 3,7; 4,6;
11:	2,9; 3,8; 4,7; 5,6;
12:	3,9; 4,8; 5,7;
13:	4,9; 5,8; 6,7;
14:	5,9; 6,8;
15:	6,9; 7,8;
16:	7,9;
17:	8,9;

CLUES OF LENGTH 3:

6:	1,2,3;
7:	1,2,4;
8:	1,2,5; 1,3,4;
9:	1,2,6; 1,3,5; 2,3,4;
10:	1,2,7; 1,3,6; 1,4,5; 2,3,5;
11:	1,2,8; 1,3,7; 1,4,6; 2,3,6; 2,4,5;
12:	1,2,9; 1,3,8; 1,4,7; 1,5,6; 2,3,7; 2,4,6; 3,4,5;
13:	1,3,9; 1,4,8; 1,5,7; 2,3,8; 2,4,7; 2,5,6; 3,4,6;
14:	1,4,9; 1,5,8; 1,6,7; 2,3,9; 2,4,8; 2,5,7; 3,4,7; 3,5,6;
15:	1,5,9; 1,6,8; 2,4,9; 2,5,8; 2,6,7; 3,4,8; 3,5,7; 4,5,6;
16:	1,6,9; 1,7,8; 2,5,9; 2,6,8; 3,4,9; 3,5,8; 3,6,7; 4,5,7;
17:	1,7,9; 2,6,9; 2,7,8; 3,5,9; 3,6,8; 4,5,8; 4,6,7;
18:	1,8,9; 2,7,9; 3,6,9; 3,7,8; 4,5,9; 4,6,8; 5,6,7;
19:	2,8,9; 3,7,9; 4,6,9; 4,7,8; 5,6,8;
20:	3,8,9; 4,7,9; 5,6,9; 5,7,8;
21:	4,8,9; 5,7,9; 6,7,8;
22:	5,8,9; 6,7,9;
23:	6,8,9;
24:	7,8,9;

CLUES OF LENGTH 4:

10: 1,2,3,4;
11: 1,2,3,5;
12: 1,2,3,6; 1,2,4,5;
13: 1,2,3,7; 1,2,4,6; 1,3,4,5;
14: 1,2,3,8; 1,2,4,7; 1,2,5,6; 1,3,4,6; 2,3,4,5;
15: 1,2,3,9; 1,2,4,8; 1,2,5,7; 1,3,4,7; 1,3,5,6; 2,3,4,6;
16: 1,2,4,9; 1,2,5,8; 1,2,6,7; 1,3,4,8; 1,3,5,7; 1,4,5,6; 2,3,4,7; 2,3,5,6;
17: 1,2,5,9; 1,2,6,8; 1,3,4,9; 1,3,5,8; 1,3,6,7; 1,4,5,7; 2,3,4,8; 2,3,5,7; 2,4,5,6;
18: 1,2,6,9; 1,2,7,8; 1,3,5,9; 1,3,6,8; 1,4,5,8; 1,4,6,7; 2,3,4,9; 2,3,5,8; 2,3,6,7; 2,4,5,7; 3,4,5,6;
19: 1,2,7,9; 1,3,6,9; 1,3,7,8; 1,4,5,9; 1,4,6,8; 1,5,6,7; 2,3,5,9; 2,3,6,8; 2,4,5,8; 2,4,6,7; 3,4,5,7;
20: 1,2,8,9; 1,3,7,9; 1,4,6,9; 1,4,7,8; 1,5,6,8; 2,3,6,9; 2,3,7,8; 2,4,5,9; 2,4,6,8; 2,5,6,7; 3,4,5,8; 3,4,6,7;
21: 1,3,8,9; 1,4,7,9; 1,5,6,9; 1,5,7,8; 2,3,7,9; 2,4,6,9; 2,4,7,8; 2,5,6,8; 3,4,5,9; 3,4,6,8; 3,5,6,7;
22: 1,4,8,9; 1,5,7,9; 1,6,7,8; 2,3,8,9; 2,4,7,9; 2,5,6,9; 2,5,7,8; 3,4,6,9; 3,4,7,8; 3,5,6,8; 4,5,6,7;
23: 1,5,8,9; 1,6,7,9; 2,4,8,9; 2,5,7,9; 2,6,7,8; 3,4,7,9; 3,5,6,9; 3,5,7,8; 4,5,6,8;
24: 1,6,8,9; 2,5,8,9; 2,6,7,9; 3,4,8,9; 3,5,7,9; 3,6,7,8; 4,5,6,9; 4,5,7,8;
25: 1,7,8,9; 2,6,8,9; 3,5,8,9; 3,6,7,9; 4,5,7,9; 4,6,7,8;
26: 2,7,8,9; 3,6,8,9; 4,5,8,9; 4,6,7,9; 5,6,7,8;
27: 3,7,8,9; 4,6,8,9; 5,6,7,9;
28: 4,7,8,9; 5,6,8,9;
29: 5,7,8,9;
30: 6,7,8,9;

CLUES OF LENGTH 5:

15: 1,2,3,4,5;

16: 1,2,3,4,6;

17: 1,2,3,4,7; 1,2,3,5,6;

18: 1,2,3,4,8; 1,2,3,5,7; 1,2,4,5,6;

19: 1,2,3,4,9; 1,2,3,5,8; 1,2,3,6,7; 1,2,4,5,7; 1,3,4,5,6;

20: 1,2,3,5,9; 1,2,3,6,8; 1,2,4,5,8; 1,2,4,6,7; 1,3,4,5,7; 2,3,4,5,6;

21: 1,2,3,6,9; 1,2,3,7,8; 1,2,4,5,9; 1,2,4,6,8; 1,2,5,6,7; 1,3,4,5,8; 1,3,4,6,7; 2,3,4,5,7;

22: 1,2,3,7,9; 1,2,4,6,9; 1,2,4,7,8; 1,2,5,6,8; 1,3,4,5,9; 1,3,4,6,8; 1,3,5,6,7; 2,3,4,5,8; 2,3,4,6,7;

23: 1,2,3,8,9; 1,2,4,7,9; 1,2,5,6,9; 1,2,5,7,8; 1,3,4,6,9; 1,3,4,7,8; 1,3,5,6,8; 1,4,5,6,7; 2,3,4,5,9; 2,3,4,6,8; 2,3,5,6,7;

24: 1,2,4,8,9; 1,2,5,7,9; 1,2,6,7,8; 1,3,4,7,9; 1,3,5,6,9; 1,3,5,7,8; 1,4,5,6,8; 2,3,4,6,9; 2,3,4,7,8; 2,3,5,6,8; 2,4,5,6,7;

25: 1,2,5,8,9; 1,2,6,7,9; 1,3,4,8,9; 1,3,5,7,9; 1,3,6,7,8; 1,4,5,6,9; 1,4,5,7,8; 2,3,4,7,9; 2,3,5,6,9; 2,3,5,7,8; 2,4,5,6,8; 3,4,5,6,7;

26: 1,2,6,8,9; 1,3,5,8,9; 1,3,6,7,9; 1,4,5,7,9; 1,4,6,7,8; 2,3,4,8,9; 2,3,5,7,9; 2,3,6,7,8; 2,4,5,6,9; 2,4,5,7,8; 3,4,5,6,8;

27: 1,2,7,8,9; 1,3,6,8,9; 1,4,5,8,9; 1,4,6,7,9; 1,5,6,7,8; 2,3,5,8,9; 2,3,6,7,9; 2,4,5,7,9; 2,4,6,7,8; 3,4,5,6,9; 3,4,5,7,8;

28: 1,3,7,8,9; 1,4,6,8,9; 1,5,6,7,9; 2,3,6,8,9; 2,4,5,8,9; 2,4,6,7,9; 2,5,6,7,8; 3,4,5,7,9; 3,4,6,7,8;

29: 1,4,7,8,9; 1,5,6,8,9; 2,3,7,8,9; 2,4,6,8,9; 2,5,6,7,9; 3,4,5,8,9; 3,4,6,7,9; 3,5,6,7,8;

30: 1,5,7,8,9; 2,4,7,8,9; 2,5,6,8,9; 3,4,6,8,9; 3,5,6,7,9; 4,5,6,7,8;

31: 1,6,7,8,9; 2,5,7,8,9; 3,4,7,8,9; 3,5,6,8,9; 4,5,6,7,9;

32: 2,6,7,8,9; 3,5,7,8,9; 4,5,6,8,9;

33: 3,6,7,8,9; 4,5,7,8,9;

34: 4,6,7,8,9;

35: 5,6,7,8,9;

CLUES OF LENGTH 6:

21: 1,2,3,4,5,6;
22: 1,2,3,4,5,7;
23: 1,2,3,4,5,8; 1,2,3,4,6,7;
24: 1,2,3,4,5,9; 1,2,3,4,6,8; 1,2,3,5,6,7;
25: 1,2,3,4,6,9; 1,2,3,4,7,8; 1,2,3,5,6,8; 1,2,4,5,6,7;
26: 1,2,3,4,7,9; 1,2,3,5,6,9; 1,2,3,5,7,8; 1,2,4,5,6,8; 1,3,4,5,6,7;
27: 1,2,3,4,8,9; 1,2,3,5,7,9; 1,2,3,6,7,8; 1,2,4,5,6,9; 1,2,4,5,7,8; 1,3,4,5,6,8; 2,3,4,5,6,7;
28: 1,2,3,5,8,9; 1,2,3,6,7,9; 1,2,4,5,7,9; 1,2,4,6,7,8; 1,3,4,5,6,9; 1,3,4,5,7,8; 2,3,4,5,6,8;
29: 1,2,3,6,8,9; 1,2,4,5,8,9; 1,2,4,6,7,9; 1,2,5,6,7,8; 1,3,4,5,7,9; 1,3,4,6,7,8; 2,3,4,5,6,9; 2,3,4,5,7,8;
30: 1,2,3,7,8,9; 1,2,4,6,8,9; 1,2,5,6,7,9; 1,3,4,5,8,9; 1,3,4,6,7,9; 1,3,5,6,7,8; 2,3,4,5,7,9; 2,3,4,6,7,8;
31: 1,2,4,7,8,9; 1,2,5,6,8,9; 1,3,4,6,8,9; 1,3,5,6,7,9; 1,4,5,6,7,8; 2,3,4,5,8,9; 2,3,4,6,7,9; 2,3,5,6,7,8;
32: 1,2,5,7,8,9; 1,3,4,7,8,9; 1,3,5,6,8,9; 1,4,5,6,7,9; 2,3,4,6,8,9; 2,3,5,6,7,9; 2,4,5,6,7,8;
33: 1,2,6,7,8,9; 1,3,5,7,8,9; 1,4,5,6,8,9; 2,3,4,7,8,9; 2,3,5,6,8,9; 2,4,5,6,7,9; 3,4,5,6,7,8;
34: 1,3,6,7,8,9; 1,4,5,7,8,9; 2,3,5,7,8,9; 2,4,5,6,8,9; 3,4,5,6,7,9;
35: 1,4,6,7,8,9; 2,3,6,7,8,9; 2,4,5,7,8,9; 3,4,5,6,8,9;
36: 1,5,6,7,8,9; 2,4,6,7,8,9; 3,4,5,7,8,9;
37: 2,5,6,7,8,9; 3,4,6,7,8,9;
38: 3,5,6,7,8,9;
39: 4,5,6,7,8,9;

Level 1

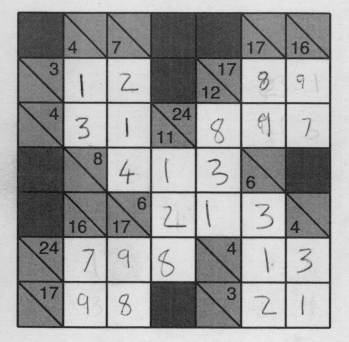

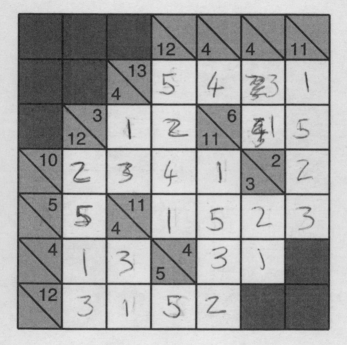

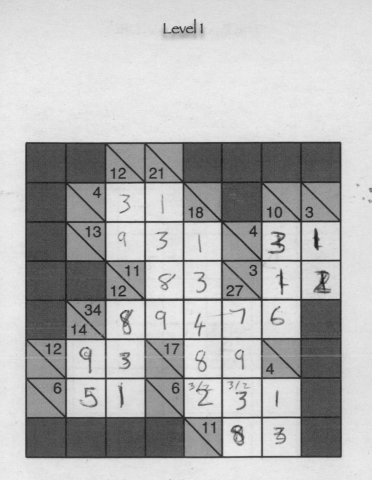

4789

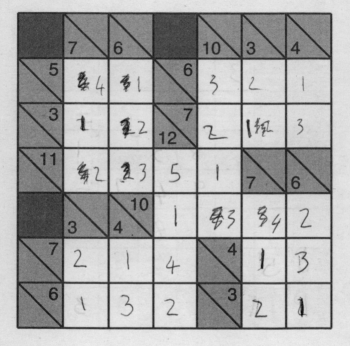

The grid (Puzzle 5):

	7	6		10	3	4
5	4	1	6	3	2	1
3	1	2	7 / 12	2	1	3
11	2	3	5	1	7	6
	3	4 / 10	1	3	4	2
7	2	1	4	4	1	3
6	1	3	2	3	2	1

X wrong.

PUZZLE 5

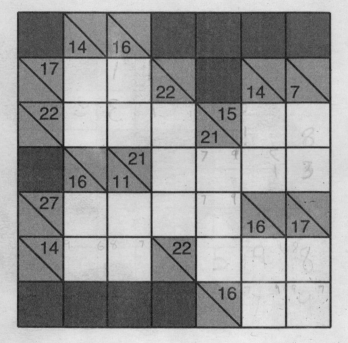

Level 1

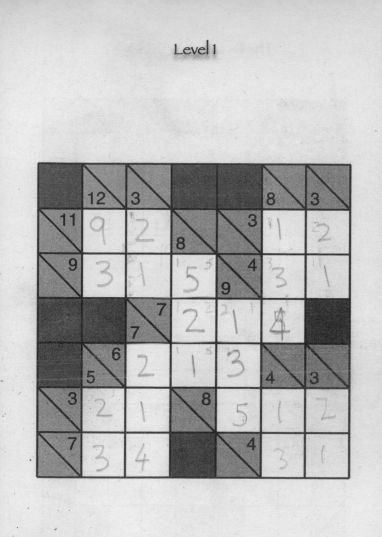

PUZZLE 8

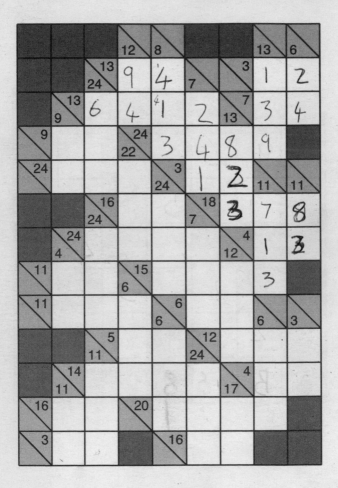

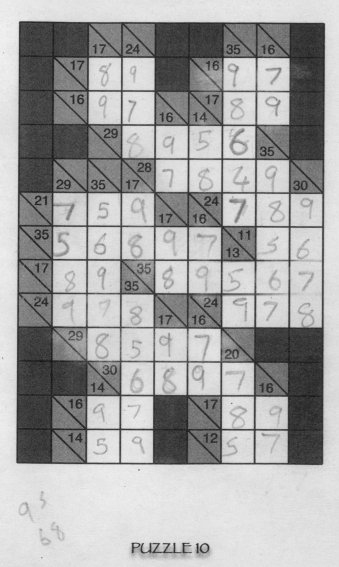

The Book of KAKURO

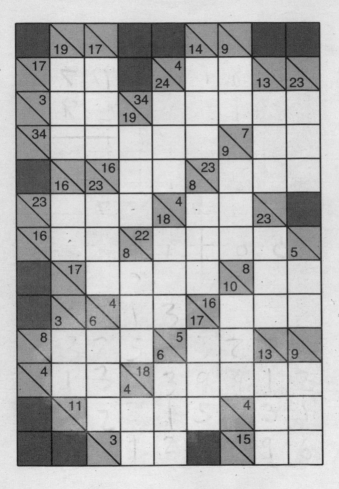

PUZZLE 11

The Book of KAKURO

PUZZLE 13

Level 1

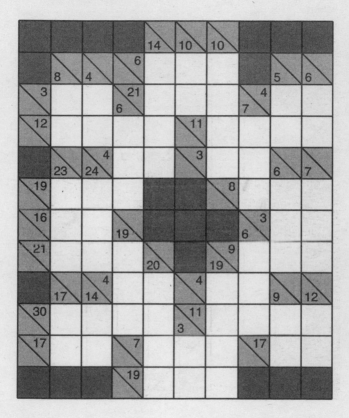

PUZZLE 14

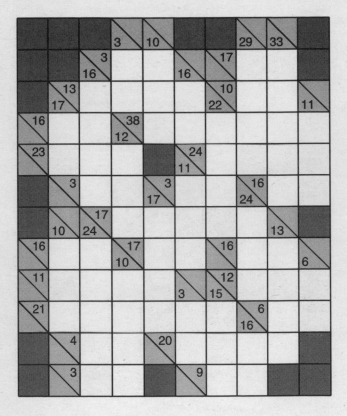

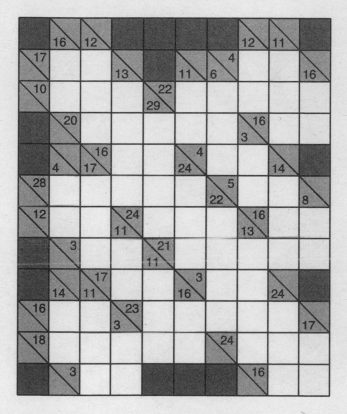

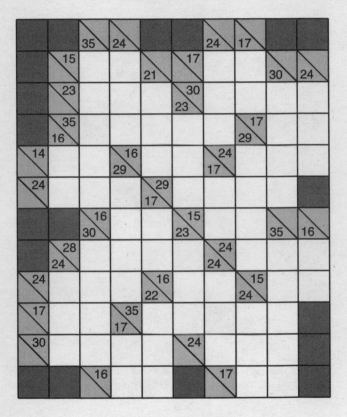

Level 1

PUZZLE 18

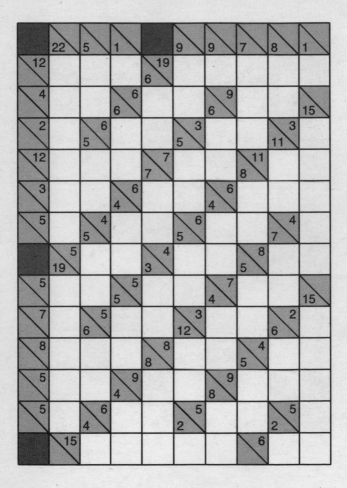

Level 1

PUZZLE 20

The Book of KAKURO

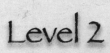

Level 2

The Book of KAKURO

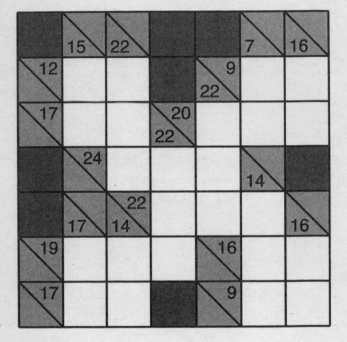

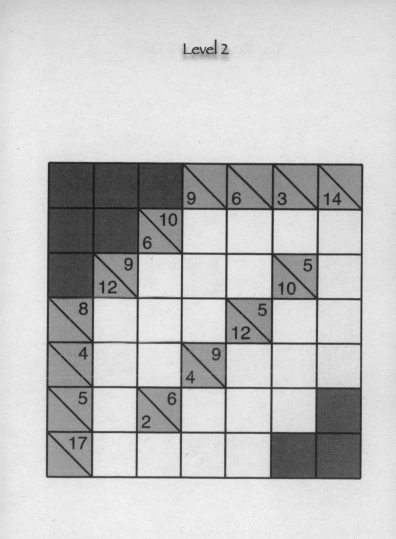

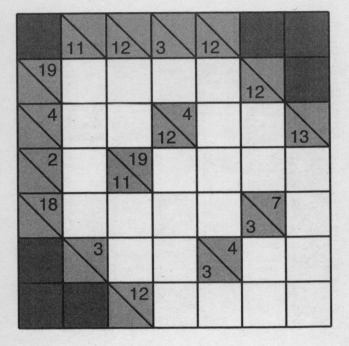

Level 2

PUZZLE 25

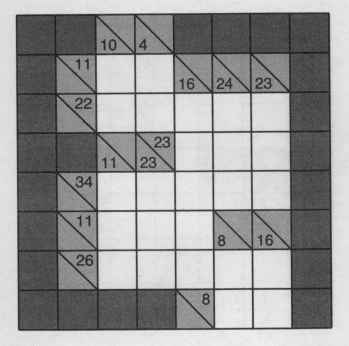

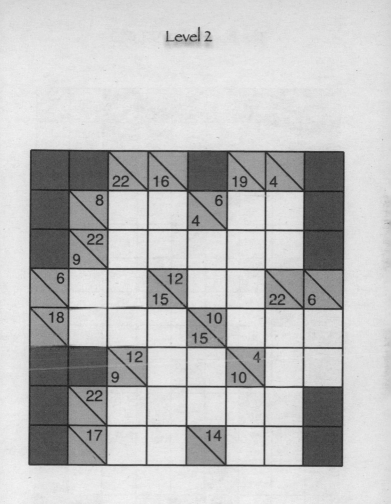

PUZZLE 27

The Book of KAKURO

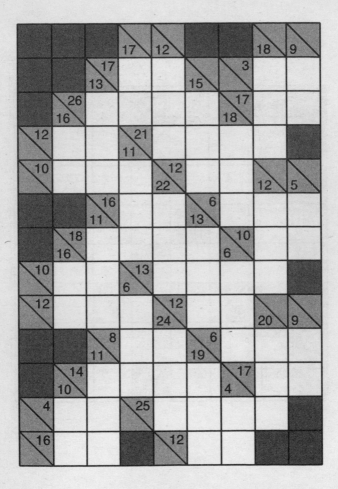

Level 2

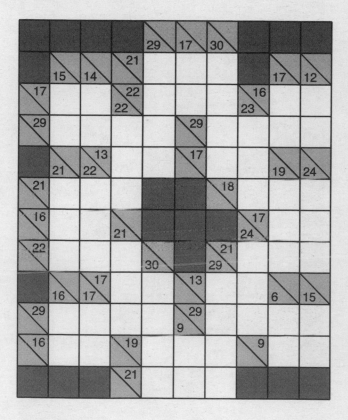

The Book of KAKURO

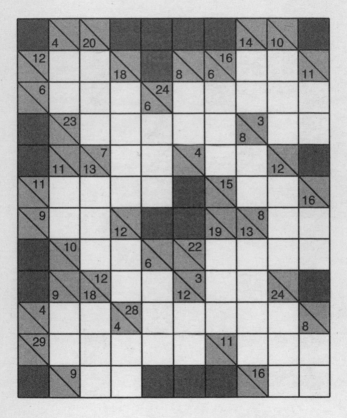

PUZZLE 30

Level 2

PUZZLE 31

The Book of KAKURO

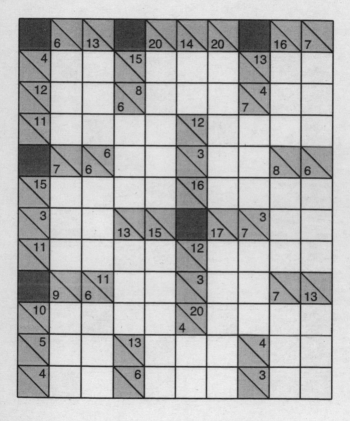

Level 2

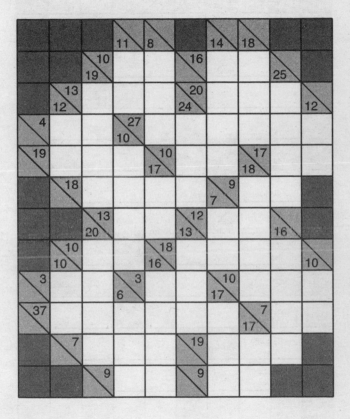

The Book of KAKURO

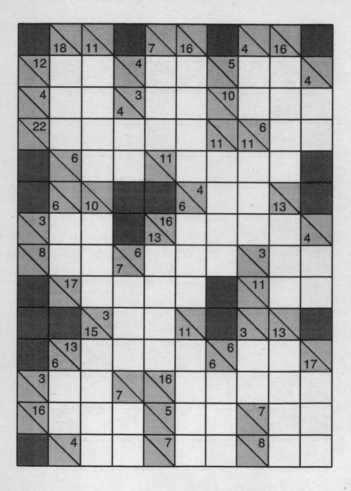

Level 2

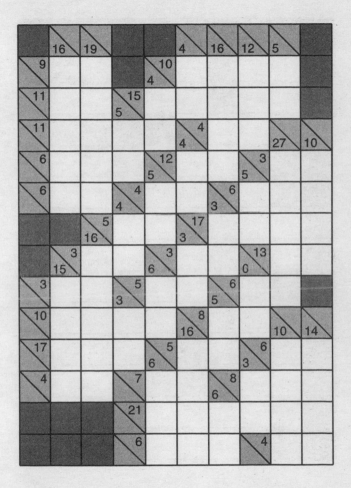

PUZZLE 35

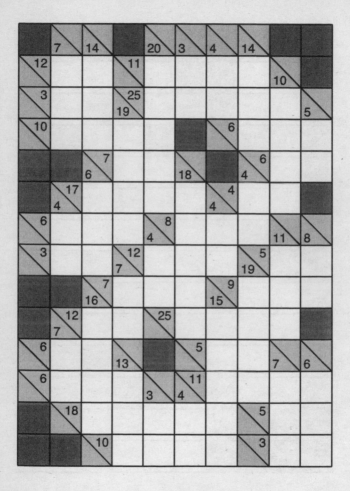

Level 2

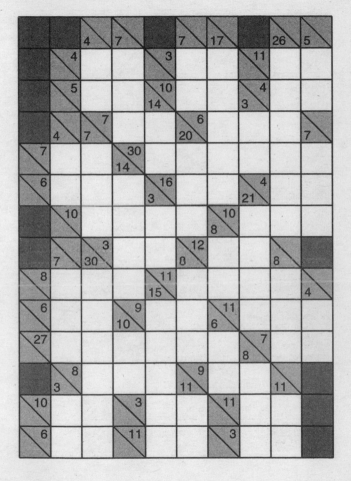

PUZZLE 37

The Book of KAKURO

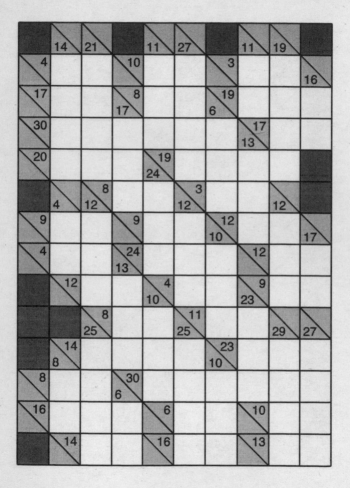

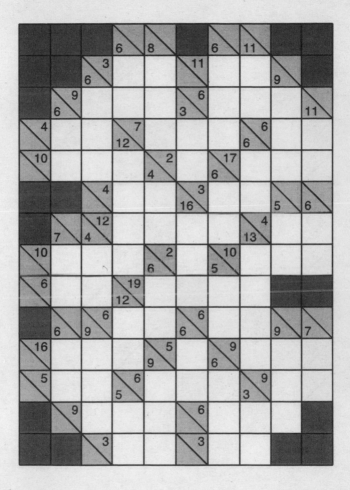

The Book of KAKURO

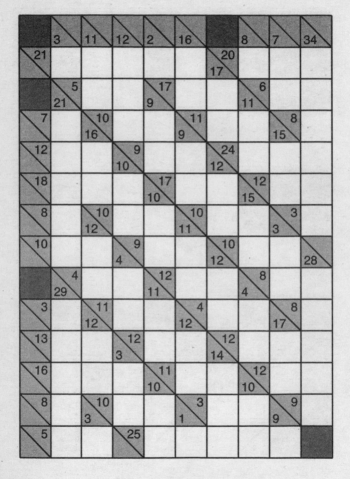

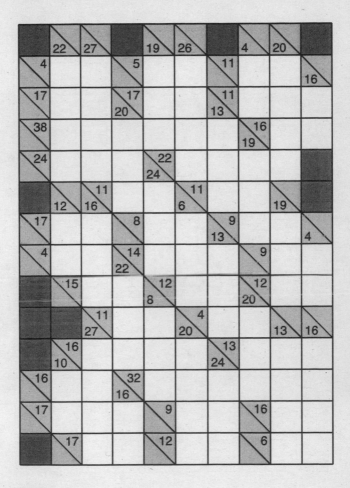

Level 3

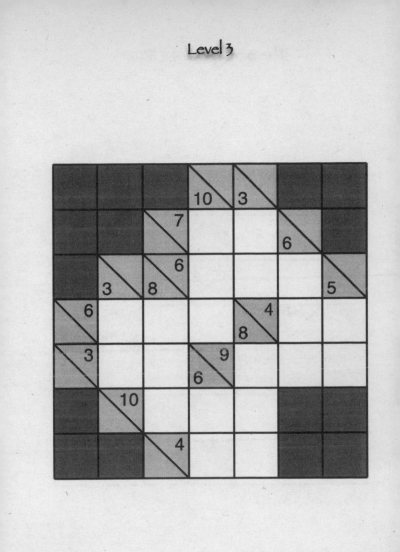

The Book of KAKURO

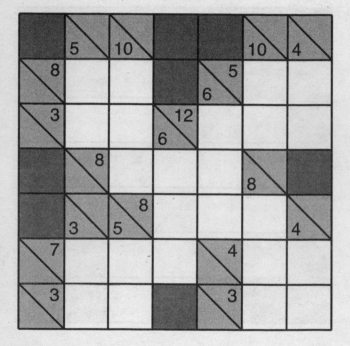

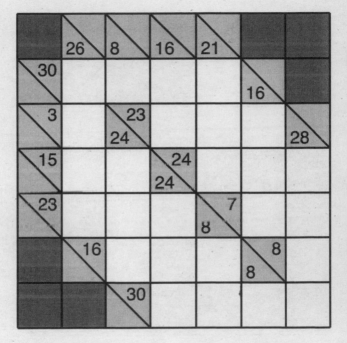

The Book of KAKURO

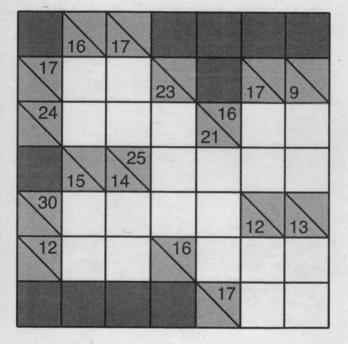

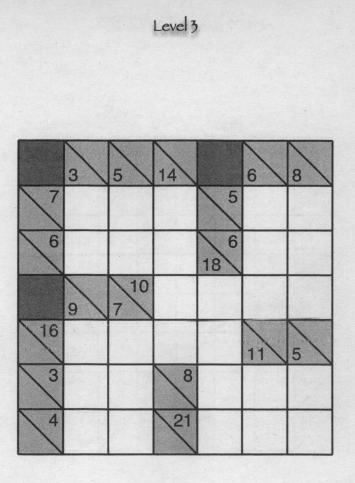

The Book of KAKURO

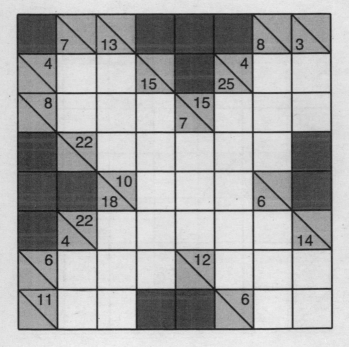

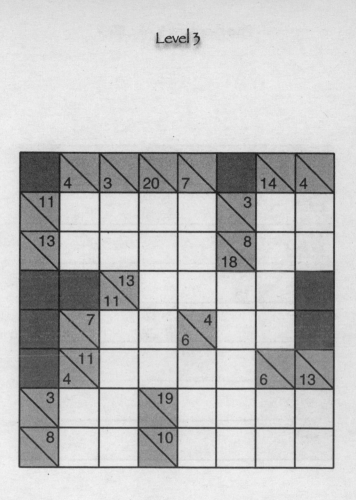

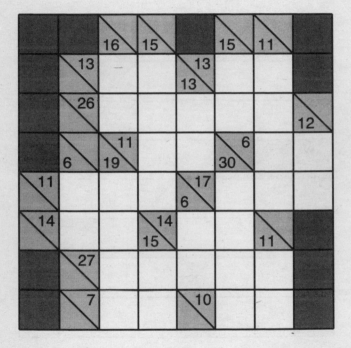

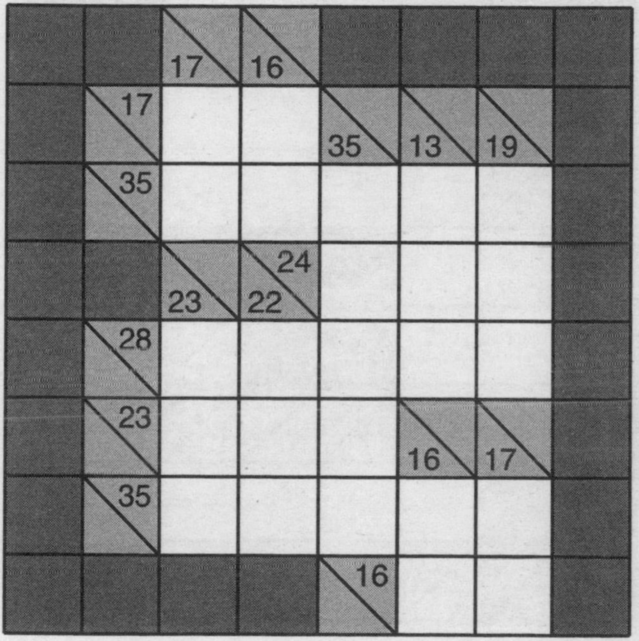
17
16
17
35
13
19
35
24
23
22
28
23
16
17
35
16

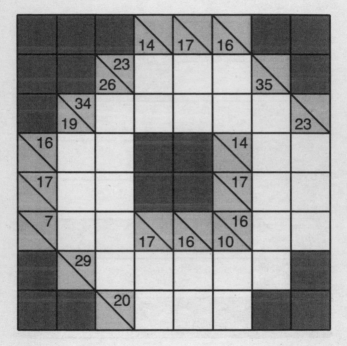

Level 3

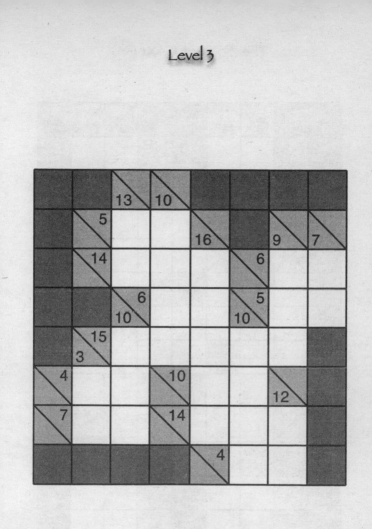

PUZZLE 52

The Book of KAKURO

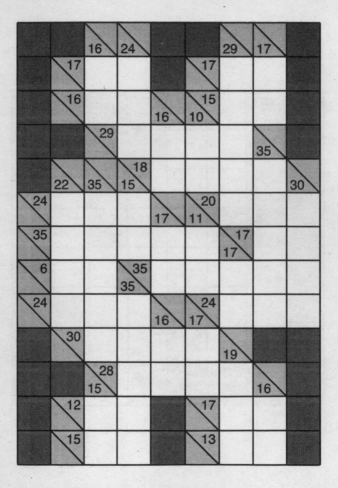

Level 3

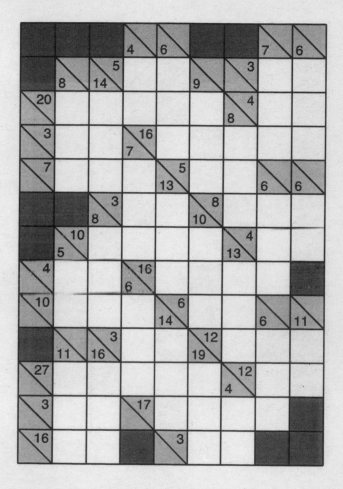

PUZZLE 54

The Book of KAKURO

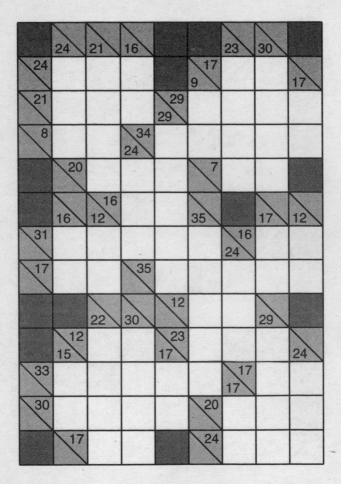

Level 3

PUZZLE 56

The Book of KAKURO

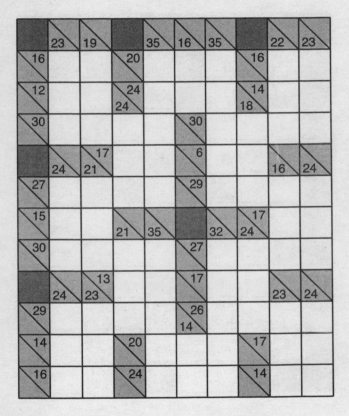

PUZZLE 57

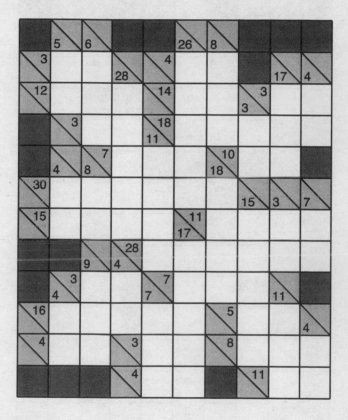

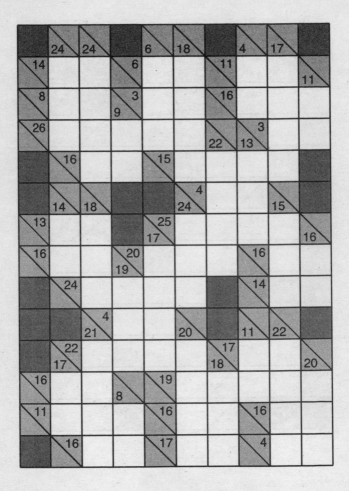

Level 3

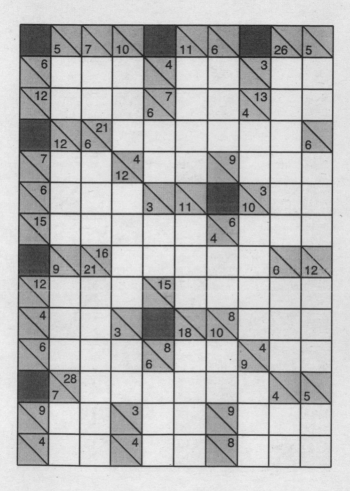

PUZZLE 60

The Book of KAKURO

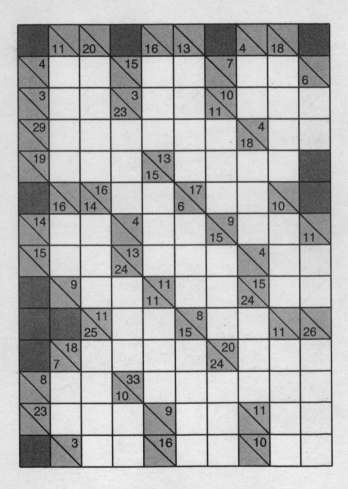

Level 4

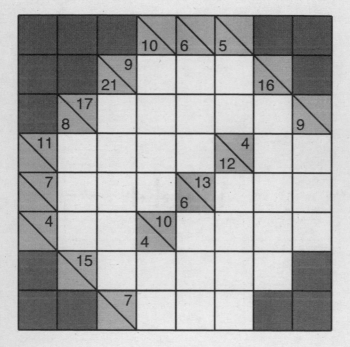

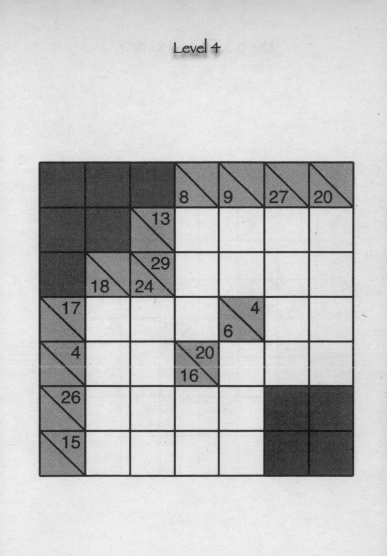

The Book of KAKURO

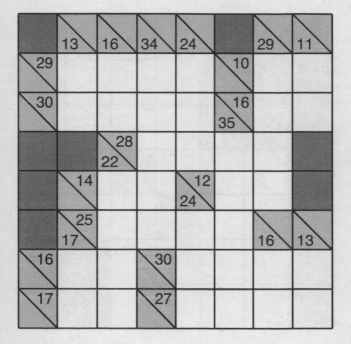

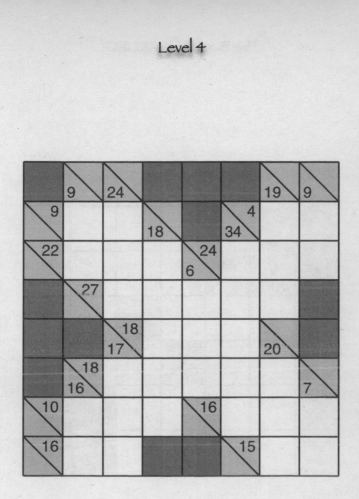

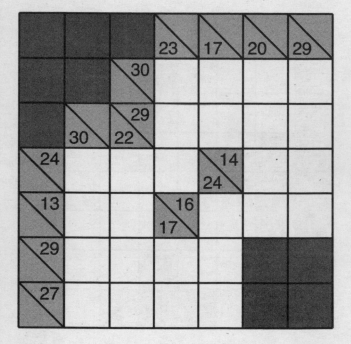

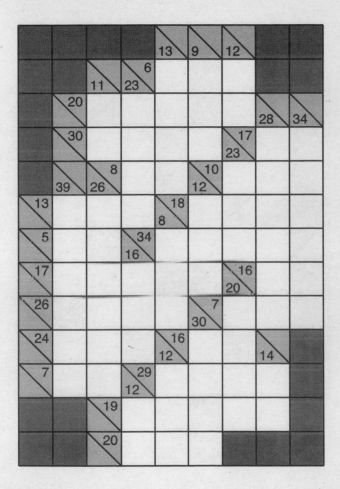

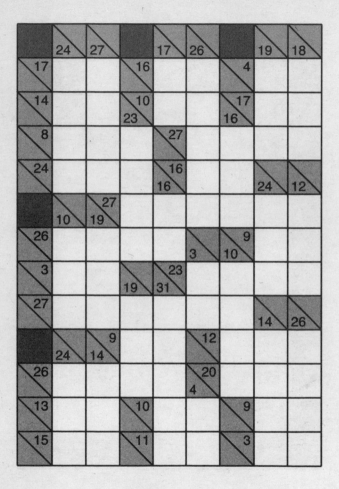

The Book of KAKURO

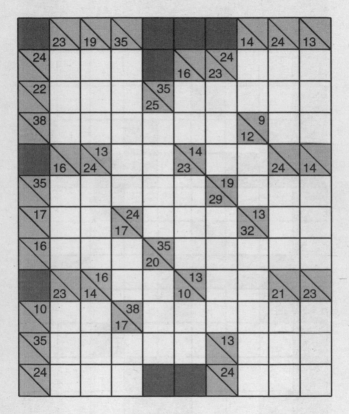

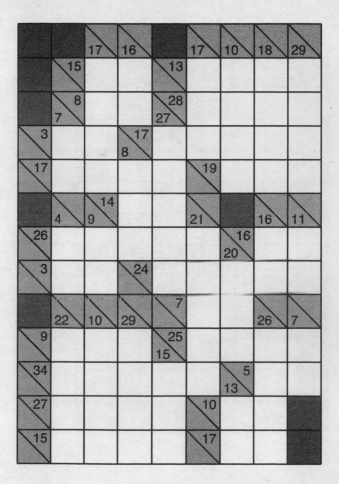

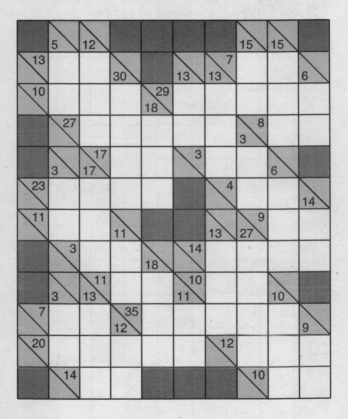

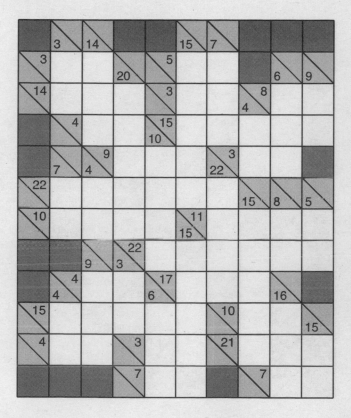

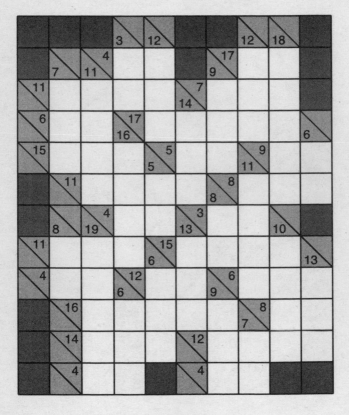

PUZZLE 74

Level 4

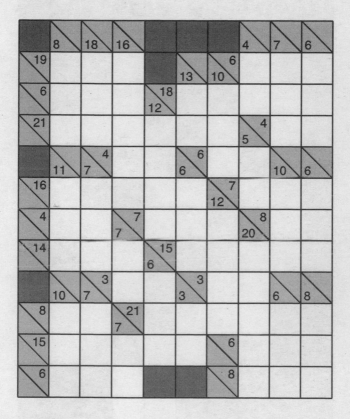

The Book of KAKURO

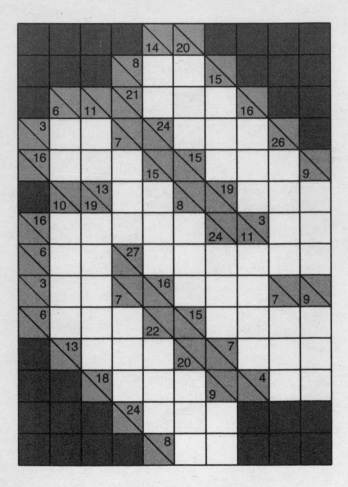

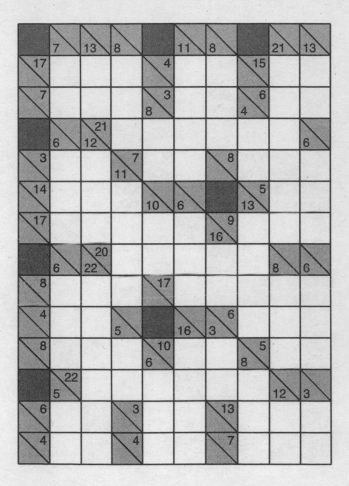

The Book of KAKURO

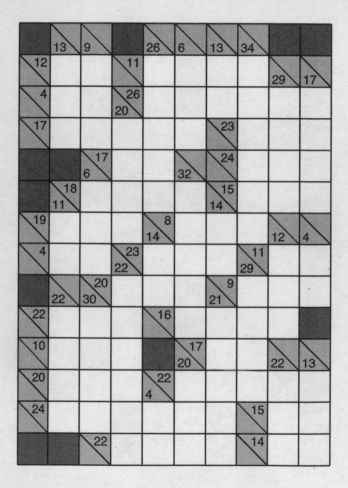

Level 4

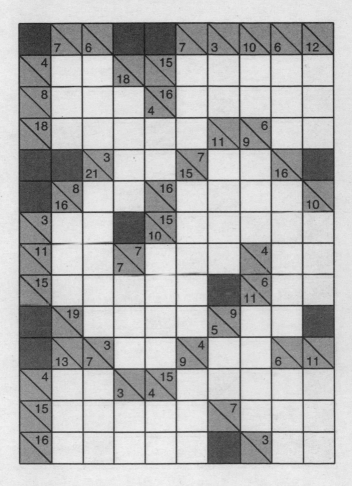

PUZZLE 79

The Book of KAKURO

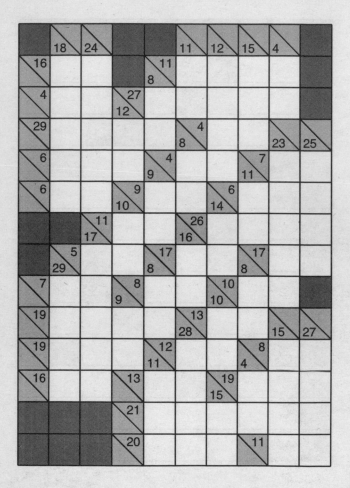

Level 4

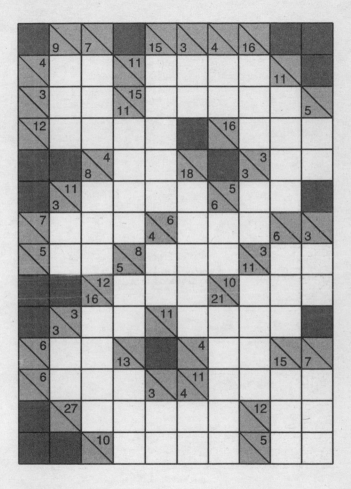

PUZZLE 81

Level 5

Level 5

PUZZLE 82

The Book of KAKURO

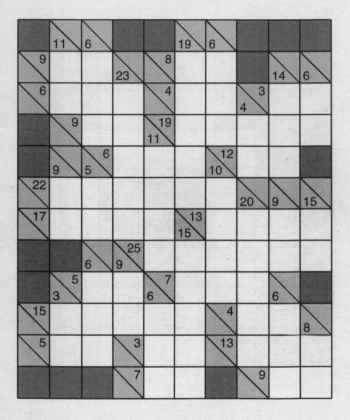

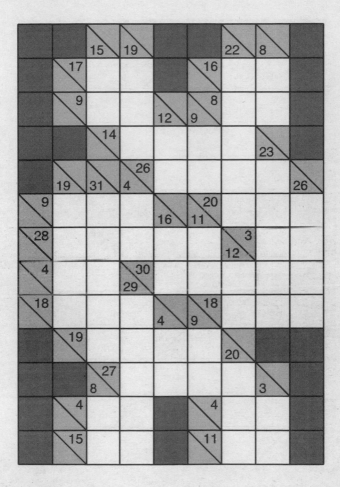

The Book of KAKURO

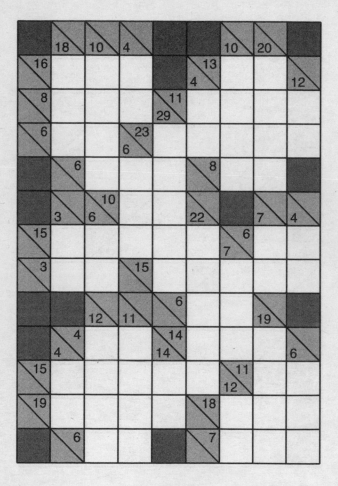

Level 5

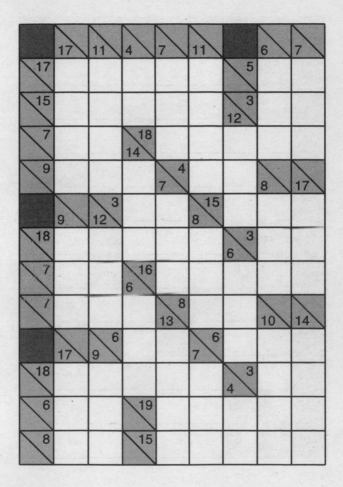

PUZZLE 86

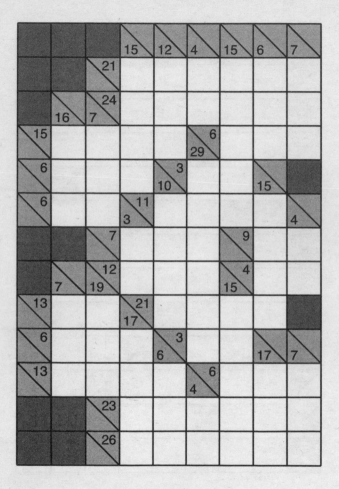

Level 5

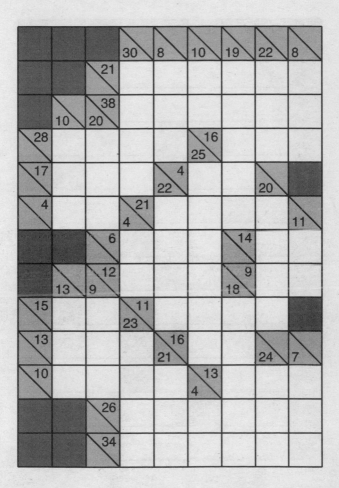

The Book of KAKURO

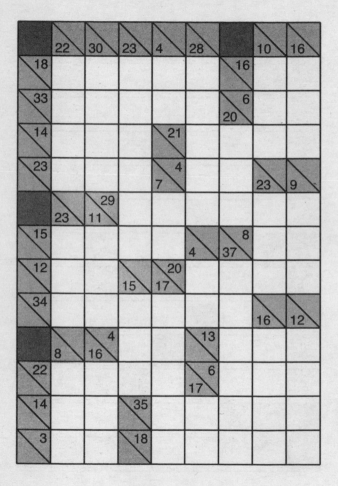

Level 5

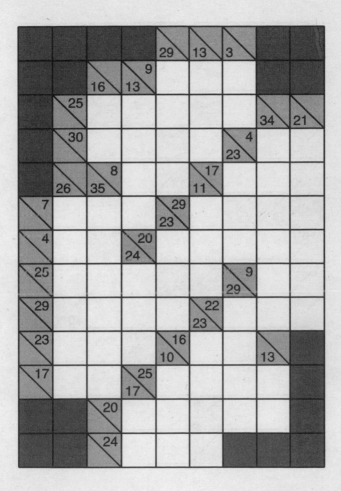

PUZZLE 90

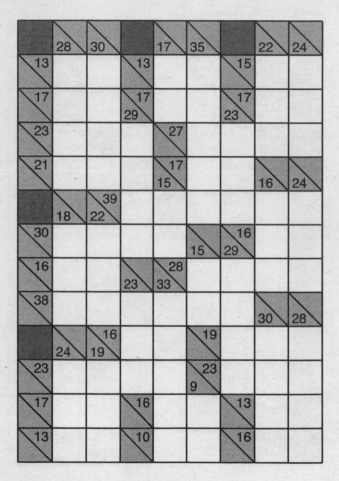

Level 5

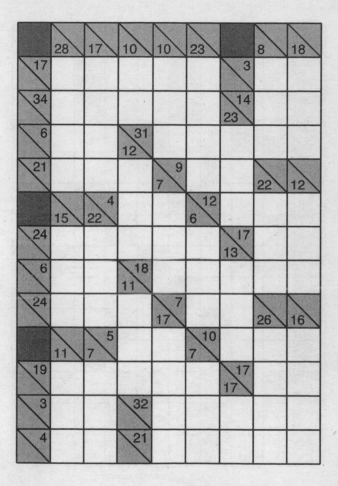

The Book of KAKURO

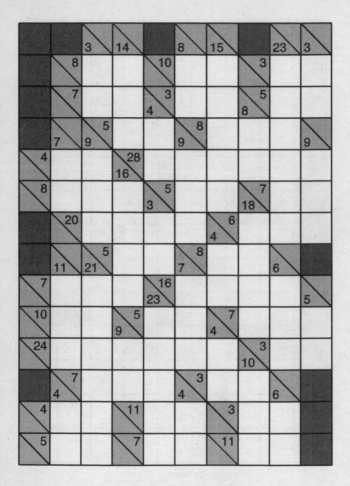

Level 5

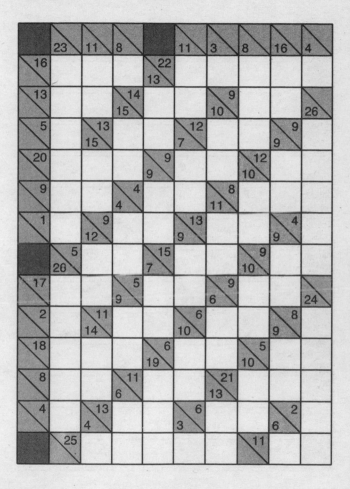

PUZZLE 94

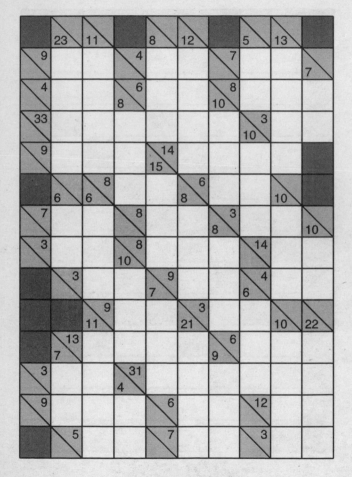

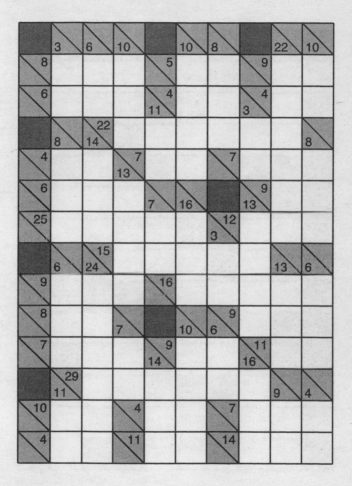

The Book of KAKURO

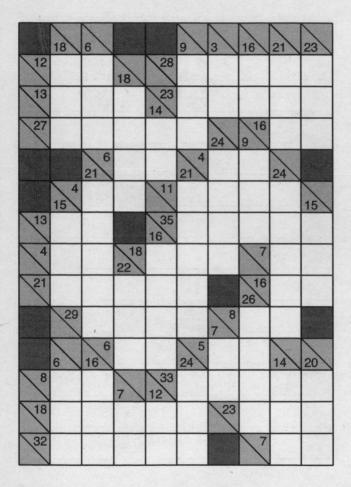

Level 5

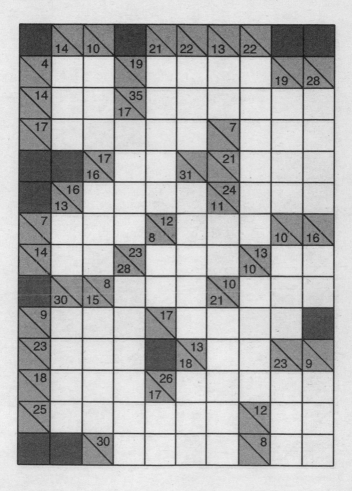

PUZZLE 98

The Book of KAKURO

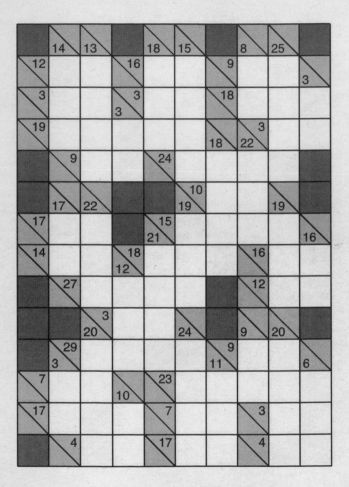

PUZZLE 99

Level 5

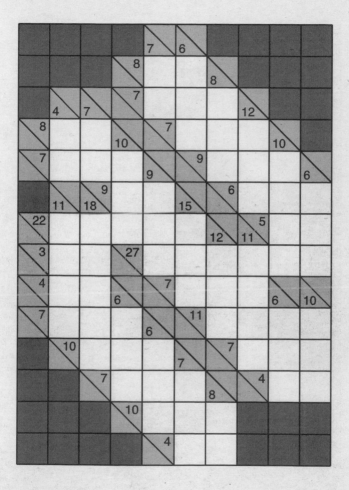

The Book of KAKURO

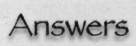

Answers

ANSWERS

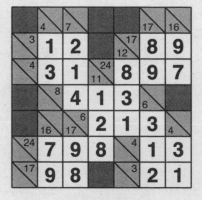

PUZZLE 1

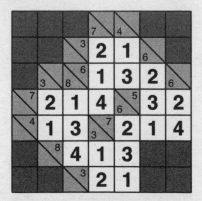

PUZZLE 2

ANSWERS

PUZZLE 3

			12	4	4	11
		13/4	5	4	3	1
	3/12	1	2	6/11	1	5
10	2	3	4	1	2/3	2
5	5	11/4	1	5	2	3
4	1	3	4/5	3	1	
12	4	1	5	2		

PUZZLE 4

		12	21			10	3
	4	3	1	18		10	3
	13	9	3	1	4	3	1
	11/12	8	3	3/27	1	2	
34/14	8	9	4	7	6		
12	9	3	17	8	9	4	
6	5	1	6	2	3	1	
			11	8	3		

ANSWERS

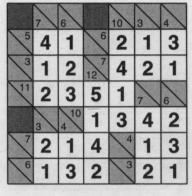

PUZZLE 5

PUZZLE 6

ANSWERS

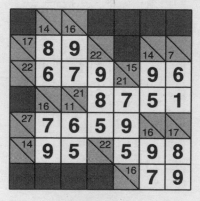

PUZZLE 7

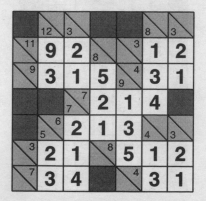

PUZZLE 8

ANSWERS

PUZZLE 9

PUZZLE 10

ANSWERS

PUZZLE 11

	19	17			14	9		
17	8	9	24/4	1	3	13	23	
3	2	1	19/34	9	7	6	4	8
34	9	7	4	8	6	9/7	1	6
	16/	23/16	9	7	8/23	6	8	9
23	9	8	6	18/4	3	1	23	
16	7	9	8/22	7	4	2	9	5
	17	6	2	8	1	10/8	6	2
3	6/	4	1	3	17/16	5	8	3
8	2	1	5	6/5	4	1	13	9
4	1	3	4/18	3	8	4	1	2
	11	2	3	1	5	4	3	1
		3	1	2		15	9	6

PUZZLE 12

			4	7		22	20		
		19/5	3	2	4	1	3	15	
	14/7	2	1	4	24/19	8	9	2	17
16	9	7	24/35	1	7	6	8	4	9
21	5	9	7	17/16	9	7	21/9	1	8
	24	1	6	9	8	3/17	9	8	
	11/17	9	8	23/3	2	1	25	
10/3	1	2	16/12	6	1	3	2	16
4	1	3	7/17	8	9	22/23	8	6	9
34	9	5	2	4	8	6	15/15	8	7
	7	2	4	1	24	7	8	9	
		4	1	3	16	9	7		

ANSWERS

PUZZLE 13

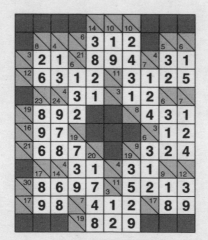

PUZZLE 14

ANSWERS

PUZZLE 15

PUZZLE 16

ANSWERS

PUZZLE 17

PUZZLE 18

ANSWERS

PUZZLE 19

PUZZLE 20

ANSWERS

PUZZLE 21

PUZZLE 22

ANSWERS

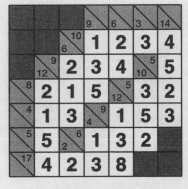

PUZZLE 23

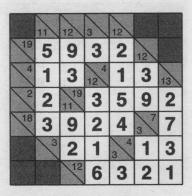

PUZZLE 24

ANSWERS

PUZZLE 25

	16	7			22	15
9	7	2	22	12	5	7
20	9	5	6	17 22	9	8
		24 14	7	9	8	
	22 16	5	9	8	14	17
16	9	7	19	5	6	8
9	7	2		17	8	9

PUZZLE 26

		10	4				
	11	8	3	16	24	23	
	22	2	1	3	7	9	
		11 23	23	6	9	8	
	34	7	9	4	8	6	
	11	1	8	2	8	16	
	26	3	6	1	7	9	
				8	1	7	

ANSWERS

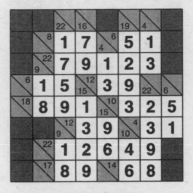

PUZZLE 27

PUZZLE 28

ANSWERS

PUZZLE 29

PUZZLE 30

ANSWERS

PUZZLE 31

PUZZLE 32

ANSWERS

PUZZLE 33

PUZZLE 34

ANSWERS

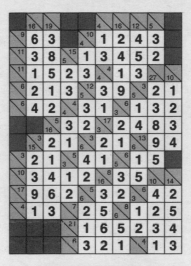

PUZZLE 35

PUZZLE 36

ANSWERS

PUZZLE 37

PUZZLE 38

ANSWERS

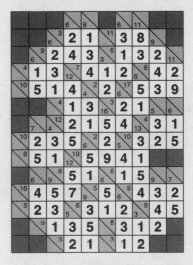

PUZZLE 39

PUZZLE 40

ANSWERS

PUZZLE 41

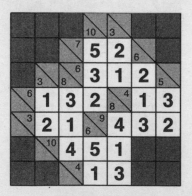

PUZZLE 42

ANSWERS

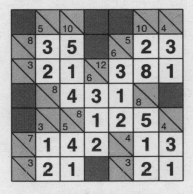

PUZZLE 43

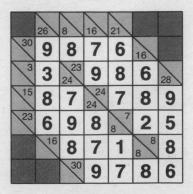

PUZZLE 44

ANSWERS

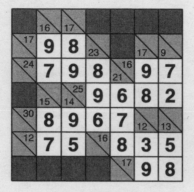

PUZZLE 45

PUZZLE 46

ANSWERS

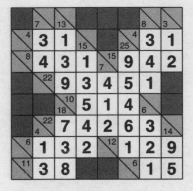

PUZZLE 47

PUZZLE 48

ANSWERS

PUZZLE 49

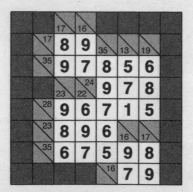

PUZZLE 50

ANSWERS

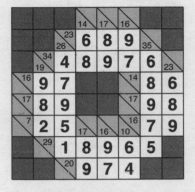

PUZZLE 51

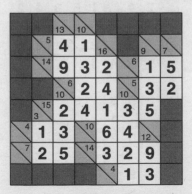

PUZZLE 52

ANSWERS

PUZZLE 53

		16	24			29	17	
	17	9	8		17	8	9	
	16	7	9	16	15 10	7	8	
		29	7	9	8	5	35	
	22	35	18 15	7	2	3	6	30
24	9	7	8	17	20 11	6	5	9
35	5	9	7	8	6	17 17	9	8
6	1	5	35 35	9	5	8	7	6
24	7	8	9	16	24 17	9	8	7
	30	6	8	7	9	19		
	28 15	6	9	8	5	16		
	12	7	5		17	8	9	
	15	8	7		13	6	7	

PUZZLE 54

			4		6			7	6
	8	5 14	3	2		9	3	2	1
20	5	9	1	3	2	8 4	1	3
3	2	1	16 7	1	6	3	4	2
7	1	4	2	5 13	1	4	6	
	8 3	1	2	8 10	1	2	5	
10 5	2	4	3	1	13 4	3	1	
4	3	1	16 6	8	4	3	1	
10	2	5	3	14	6	5	1	6 11
	11 16	3	1	2	12 19	9	1	2
27	3	5	2	8	9	12 4	3	9
3	1	2	17	4	8	3	2	
16	7	9		3	2	1		

PUZZLE 54

ANSWERS

PUZZLE 55

Row 1: **8 7 9** · · **9 8**
Row 2: **9 5 7** · **5 7 9 8**
Row 3: **7 1** · **8 4 6 7 9**
Row 4: **8 7 5** · **1 6**
Row 5: **9 7**
Row 6: **7 4 8 3 9** · **9 7**
Row 7: **9 8** · **6 7 9 8 5**
Row 8: **5 7**
Row 9: **4 8** · **6 8 9**
Row 10: **6 3 7 9 8** · **8 9**
Row 11: **9 7 6 8** · **8 5 7**
Row 12: **8 9** · **9 7 8**

PUZZLE 56

Row 1: **8 9** · **9 5**
Row 2: **5 8** · **9 7 1 8**
Row 3: **3 6 5 9 7 8** · **2 7**
Row 4: **9 7 6 8** · **5 6 9**
Row 5: **8 9** · **7 5** · **7 9**
Row 6: **9 5 2 8 4**
Row 7: **9 7** · **8 9** · **6 8**
Row 8: **9 6 8** · **6 8 9 7**
Row 9: **7 8** · **6 5 7 3 8 9**
Row 10: **5 7 9 8** · **9 7**
Row 11: **5 8** · **7 5**

ANSWERS

PUZZLE 57

PUZZLE 58

ANSWERS

PUZZLE 59

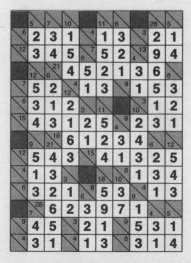

PUZZLE 60

ANSWERS

PUZZLE 61

PUZZLE 62

ANSWERS

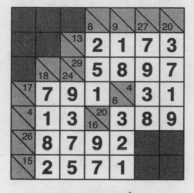

PUZZLE 63

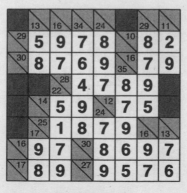

PUZZLE 64

ANSWERS

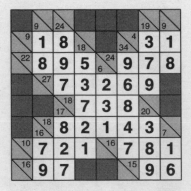

PUZZLE 65

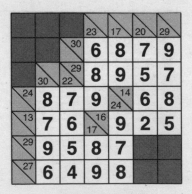

PUZZLE 66

ANSWERS

PUZZLE 67

PUZZLE 68

ANSWERS

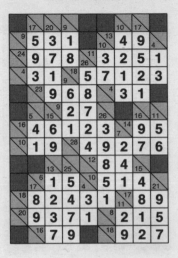

PUZZLE 69

	17	20	9			10	17	
9	5	3	1	13 / 10	4	9	4
24	9	7	8	11 / 26	3	2	5	1
4	3	1	18 / 9	5	7	1	2	3
	23	9	6	8	4	3	1	
	5	15 / 9	2	7	26		16	11
16	4	6	1	2	3	14 / 7	9	5
10	1	9	28	4	9	2	7	6
		13	25	12	8	4	15	
	6 / 17	1	5	10 / 4	5	1	4	21
18	8	2	4	3	1	17 / 11	8	9
20	9	3	7	1	8	2	1	5
	16	7	9		18	9	2	7

PUZZLE 70

	23	19	35			14	24	13
24	9	7	8		16 / 23	8	9	7
22	6	9	7	35 / 25	9	8	6	7	5
38	8	3	5	9	7	6	9 / 12	8	1
	16	13 / 24	9	4	14 / 23	9	5	24	14
35	7	8	6	5	9	19 / 29	7	9	3
17	8	9	24 / 17	7	8	9	13 / 32	7	6
16	1	7	8	35 / 20	6	7	9	8	5
	23	16 / 14	9	7	13 / 10	5	8	21	23
10	8	2	38 / 17	5	3	8	6	7	9
35	6	5	9	8	7	13	2	5	6
24	9	7	8			24	7	9	8

ANSWERS

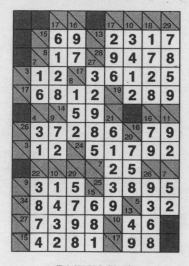

PUZZLE 71

PUZZLE 72

ANSWERS

PUZZLE 73

PUZZLE 74

ANSWERS

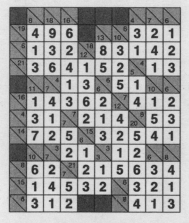

PUZZLE 75

PUZZLE 76

ANSWERS

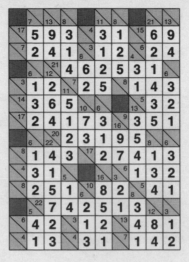

PUZZLE 77

PUZZLE 77 Grid

	7	13	8		11	8		21	13
17	5	9	3	4	3	1	15	6	9
7	2	4	1	3/8	1	2	6/4	2	4
6/12		21	4	6	2	5	3	1	6
3	1	2	7/11	2	5	8	1	4	3
14	3	6	5	10/6			5/13	3	2
17	2	4	1	7	3	9/16	3	5	1
6		20/22	2	3	1	9	5	8	6
8	1	4	3	17	2	7	4	1	3
4	3	1	5		16	3/6	1	3	2
8	2	5	1	10/6	8	2	5/8	4	1
22/5		7	4	2	5	1	3	12	3
6	4	2	3	1	2	13	4	8	1
4	1	3	4	3	1	7	1	4	2

PUZZLE 78

PUZZLE 78 Grid

	13	9		26	6	13	34		
12	8	4	11	1	2	5	3	29	17
4	1	3	26/20	3	1	8	7	5	2
17	4	2	1	7	3	23	8	9	6
		17/6	8	9	32	24	9	7	8
18/11	3	2	6	7	15/14	6	8	1
19	8	2	9	8/14	2	5	1	12	4
4	3	1	23/22	6	8	9	11/29	8	3
22	20/30	3	8	9	9/21	5	3	1
22	9	8	5	16	6	2	7	1	
10	2	7	1		17/20	9	8	22	13
20	7	9	4	22/4	3	4	9	5	1
24	4	6	2	3	8	1	15	8	7
		22	7	1	9	5	14	9	5

PUZZLE 78

ANSWERS

PUZZLE 79

PUZZLE 80

ANSWERS

PUZZLE 81

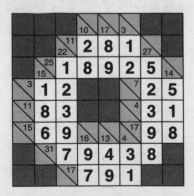

PUZZLE 82

ANSWERS

PUZZLE 83

PUZZLE 84

ANSWERS

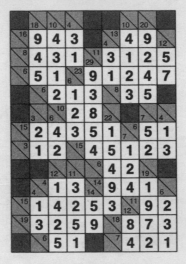

PUZZLE 85

	18	10	4			10	20	
16	9	4	3		13 / 4	4	9	12
8	4	3	1	29 / 11	3	1	2	5
6	5	1	23 / 6	9	1	2	4	7
	6	2	1	3	8	3	5	
	3	10 / 6	2	8	22		7	4
15	2	4	3	5	1	6 / 7	5	1
3	1	2	15	4	5	1	2	3
		12	11	6	4	2	19	
4 / 4		1	3	14 / 14	9	4	1	6
15	1	4	2	5	3	11 / 12	9	2
19	3	2	5	9	18	8	7	3
	6	5	1		7	4	2	1

PUZZLE 86

	17	11	4	7	11		6	7
17	7	1	3	4	2	5	1	4
15	4	5	1	2	3	12 / 3	2	1
7	5	2	18 / 14	1	5	7	3	2
9	1	3	5	7 / 4	1	3	8	17
	9	12 / 3	2	1	15 / 8	2	4	9
18	3	5	7	2	1	3 / 6	1	2
7	4	3	16 / 6	4	2	1	3	6
7	2	4	1	13 / 8	5	3	10	14
	17	9 / 6	2	4	7 / 6	2	3	1
18	8	4	3	1	2	4 / 3	1	2
6	4	2	19	5	1	3	4	6
8	5	3	15	3	4	1	2	5

ANSWERS

PUZZLE 87

PUZZLE 88

ANSWERS

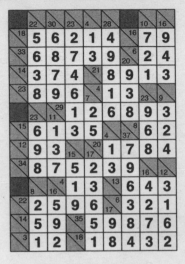

PUZZLE 89

PUZZLE 90

ANSWERS

PUZZLE 91

PUZZLE 92

ANSWERS

PUZZLE 93

PUZZLE 94

ANSWERS

PUZZLE 95

PUZZLE 96

ANSWERS

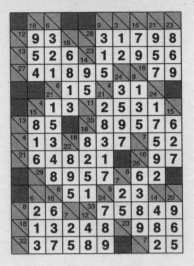

PUZZLE 97

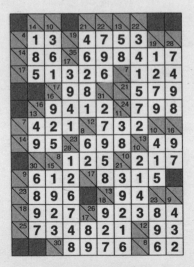

PUZZLE 98

ANSWERS

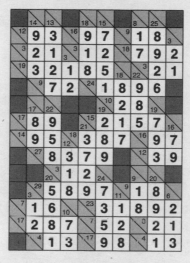

PUZZLE 99

PUZZLE 100

ANSWERS

		8	14				22	10
13/17	4	9	14	5		17/17	9	8
24	9	3	5	6	1	11/18	1	8	2
9	8	1	19/11	7	4	1	2	5
	5/9	4	1	9/8	3	6	13	8
8/13	1	7	20/27	4	5	8	2	1
7	5	2	16/12	6	1	9	12/8	5	7
27	8	6	1	9	3	11/10	5	6
	7/17	2	5	9/16	6	3	10	4
28/16	4	5	7	9	3	8/15	7	1
19	7	8	4	19	7	1	6	2	3
14	9	5			10	9	1

PUZZLE 101

For more mind-bending number puzzles, try...

The Little Book of Sudoku Pete Sinden
ISBN 1-84317-179-1 £3.99

The Little Book of Sudoku Volume Two
Pete Sinden
ISBN 1-84317-180-5 £3.99

The Little Book of Advanced Sudoku
Volume Three Alastair Chisholm
ISBN 1-84317-183-X £3.99

The Kids' Book of Sudoku! Alastair Chisholm
ISBN 1-905158-24-6 £3.99

The Kids' Book of Sudoku 2
Alastair Chisholm
ISBN 1-905158-29-7 £3.99

Shitedoku
ISBN 1-84317-182-1 £3.99

**All Michael O'Mara titles are
available by post from:**

Bookpost, PO Box 29,
Douglas, Isle of Man, IM99 1BQ
Credit cards accepted
Telephone: 01624 677237 Fax: 01624 670923
Email: bookshop@enterprise.net
Internet: www.bookpost.co.uk
Free postage and packing in the UK